HANDS-ON ART
IN THE GARDEN

KATE DAUBNEY

ARCTURUS

ARCTURUS

This edition published in 2020 by Arcturus Publishing Limited
26/27 Bickels Yard, 151–153 Bermondsey Street,
London SE1 3HA

Author: Violet Peto
Illustrator: Kate Daubney
Designer: Supriya Sahai
Art Direction: Rosie Bellwood
Managing Editor: Joe Harris

ISBN: 978-1-78950-879-6
CH007442NT
Supplier 29, Date 0820, Print run 9888

Printed in China

LET'S GET ARTY!

Follow the steps in this book to create beautiful outdoor scenes, using clever arty effects.

HANDY HINTS AND TIPS

- Before you start a picture, make sure you have your materials ready by checking the "You will need" box that appears with every project.

- For printing, pour paint into a shallow dish, and dip your printing object into it. Allow some of the paint to drip off, then press your printing object onto the paper. Try experimenting with different amounts of paint mixed with water to see which works the best.

- For blow paintings, add plenty of water to the paint to make it easy to spread.

- If you don't have one of the items used for printing, swap it for something that's a similar shape. Make sure you have an adult's help when cutting fruit and vegetables!

- To make a leaf rubbing, place a leaf under the page and rub over it with crayon.

BEAUTIFUL BLOSSOM

You will need:
Half a piece of broccoli
Paints
Cotton swabs

Cut a piece of broccoli in half lengthways, and dip the flat side in brown paint. Use this to print your tree trunk.

1

2

Make cotton swab prints to create blossoms.

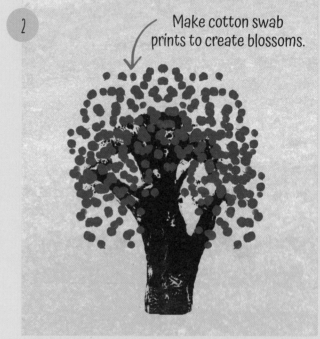

3

Try layering the blossom with different shades of pink.

4

Add a blossoming tree here for these birds to nest in.

STRING NESTS

Dip pieces of string in different shades of paint to print a bird's nest.

You will need:
String
Paints
Your fingertips
Pen

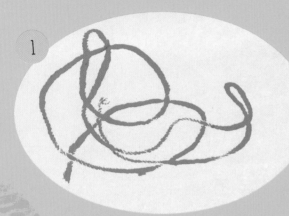
1

2

Add layers of string prints.

3

4

Add yellow fingerprints for the chicks.

5

It's time for dinner! Fill these birdhouses with hungry chicks in their nests.

SINGING BIRD

You will need:
Your hands
Paintbrush
Paints
Your fingertips
Pen

Create this sweet songbird using handprints and fingerprints.

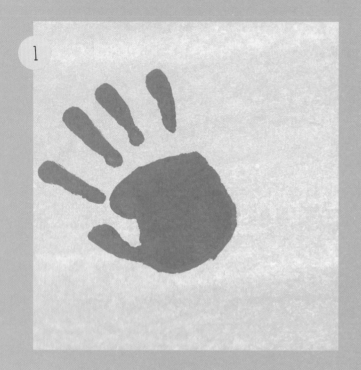

Now make a closed handprint with your thumb stretched up.

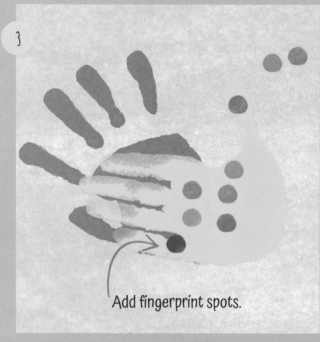

Add fingerprint spots.

Add a bird to this branch chirping a merry tune!

9

DANCING DRAGONFLY

You will need:
Leaves
Paintbrush
Paints
Your fingertips
Pen

Collect long, thin leaves in different sizes to print a beautiful dragonfly.

1

2

3

4
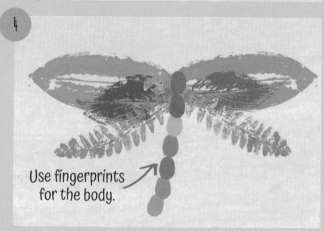

Use fingerprints for the body.

5
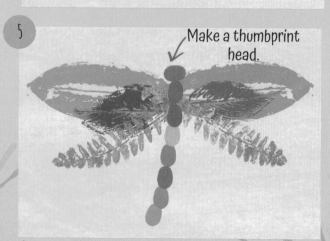

Make a thumbprint head.

6

Add more dragonflies dancing
and darting over the lily pond.

FANCY FENCES

Dip pasta pieces in paint to make fence prints.

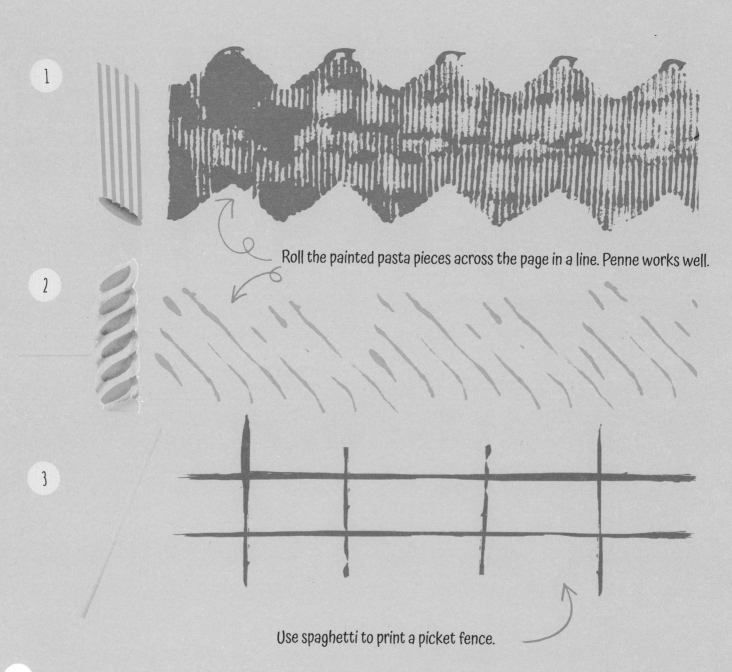

1

2

Roll the painted pasta pieces across the page in a line. Penne works well.

3

Use spaghetti to print a picket fence.

These sheep have escaped!
Add fences to pen them in.

FLOWING FOUNTAIN

You will need:
Paints
Drinking straw

This technique is a fun way to create a splashy, spray effect.

1 Arrange three blobs of different shades of watery blue paint.

2 Use a straw to blow the paint so that it spreads out and up.

3

4

Add some sprays of water
coming out of the fountain.

DABBLING DUCKS

You will need:
Your fingertips
Paints
Pen

Get your fingertips ready to create these adorable ducks! Finish with pen details.

Use a thumbprint for the body and a fingerprint for the head.

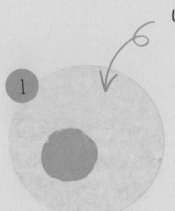

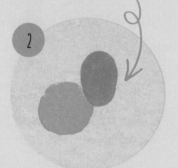

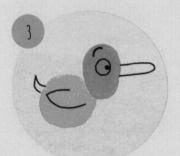

Use only the tip of your little finger for the duckling.

16

Complete the pond scene by adding some ducks splashing around.

CREEPY-CRAWLIES

Use string to print worms and centipedes. Finish with pen details.

You will need:
String
Paints
Pen

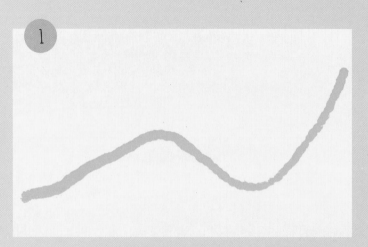

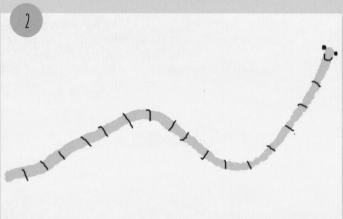

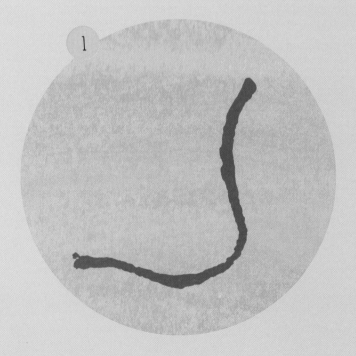

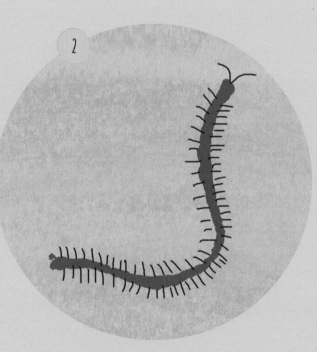

Show some wriggling worms and centipedes burrowing in the soil.

FLOWER POWER

You will need:
Empty thread reels
Paints
Paintbrush
Your fingertips
Leaves

Create pretty garden blooms by dipping a thread reel in paint and making the middle of your flower.

1

2

3

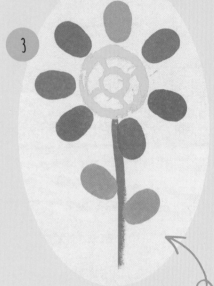

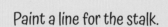

Paint a line for the stalk.

Use fingerprints for leaves and petals.

You can also use leaves to print flower shapes.

Add a row of flowers growing in the flowerpot.

OVER THE RAINBOW

Follow the steps to create a dazzling rainbow.

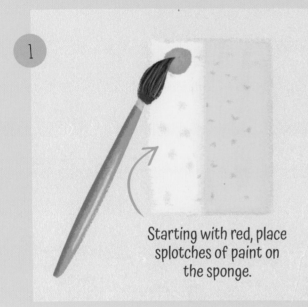

Starting with red, place splotches of paint on the sponge.

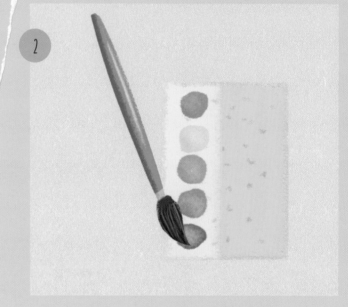

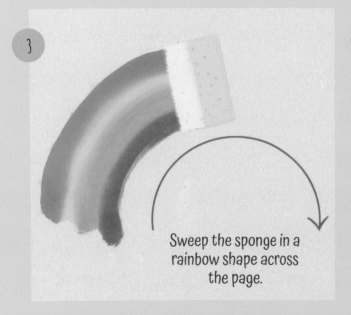

Sweep the sponge in a rainbow shape across the page.

Add a rainbow to this spring sky.

FURRY FRIENDS

You will need:
Old toothbrush
Paints
Cotton ball

Give this rabbit and lamb some warm, furry coats.

Use a toothbrush dipped in paint for the bunny's fur.

Will your lamb's wool be black or white?

Dip your cotton ball in paint, then print wool onto the lamb.

LEAFY TREE

Gather some leaves from outside, and print a leafy tree using bright, bold paints.

You will need:
Leaves
Paintbrush
Paints

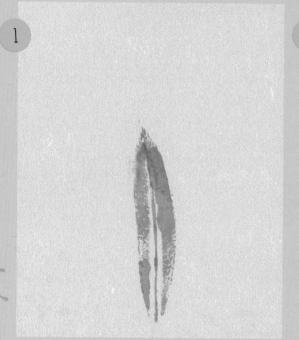

1

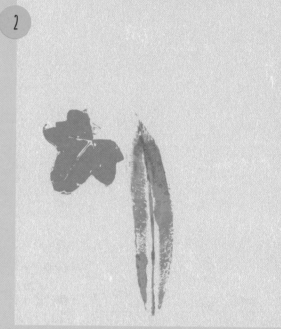

2

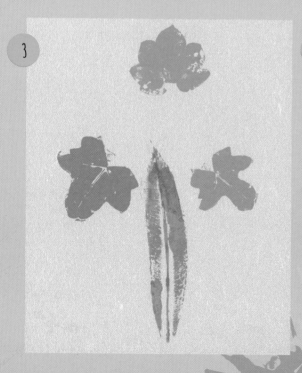

3

4

Decorate this countryside scene with trees full of leaves.

CUTE CATERPILLARS

You will need:
Thick carrot slices
Paints
Pencil
Pen

Create a cute caterpillar with carrot-slice prints.

1

2

Dip the end of a pencil in white paint for the eyes and in orange paint for the antennae.

3

Add a bunch of munching caterpillars
to these leaves.

CLIMBING CREEPERS

Blow paint with a straw to make creeping vines in bloom.

You will need:
Paints
Drinking straw
Your fingertips

1

Arrange blobs of
watery paint on
the page.

2

With the straw,
blow the blobs
of paint from
the bottom to
make the vines.

3

Use fingerprints
to add flowers
and leaves.

Make some creeping vines to climb the wall.

RED ROSE

Make pretty rose petal patterns using celery-slice prints.

You will need:
Celery slices
Paints

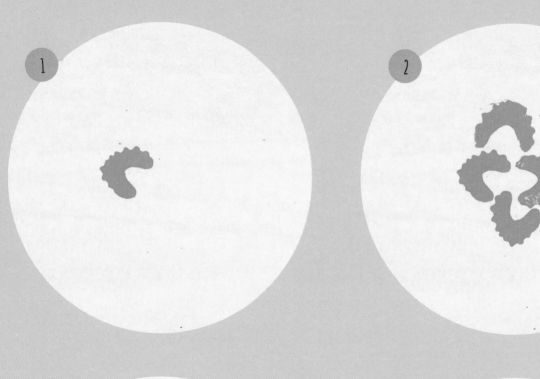

These thorny rose stems need you
to add their blooms.

FOXY FOOTPRINTS

You will need:
Your foot
Paintbrush
Paints
Your fingertips
Pen

Use your footprint to make this fantastic fox.

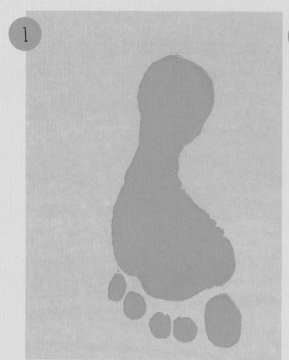

1

2

Use two orange smudged fingerprints to make ears and one for the tail.

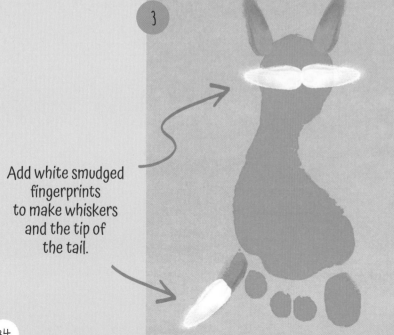

3

Add white smudged fingerprints to make whiskers and the tip of the tail.

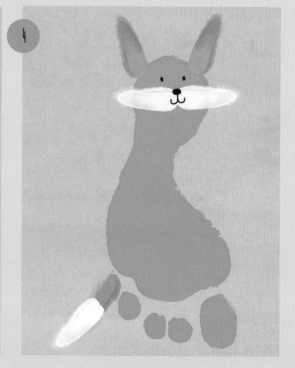

4

Add a sly fox to this night scene.

FLUTTERING BUTTERFLY

You will need:
Your fingertips
Paintbrush
Paints
Leaves
Pen

Here's how to create a beautiful butterfly with leaf-print wings.

1

2

3

Use a similar-shaped leaf for each wing.

4

Try making a handprint butterfly, too!

Add two butterflies fluttering above these bright blooms.

SHINING SUN

Use chalk and a flower print to create a brilliant Sun.

You will need:
Chalks
Paints
Flower

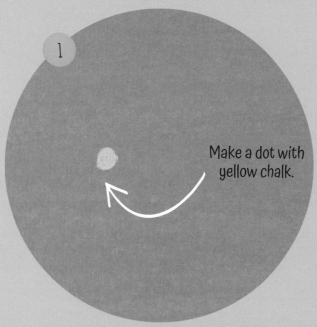

1

Make a dot with yellow chalk.

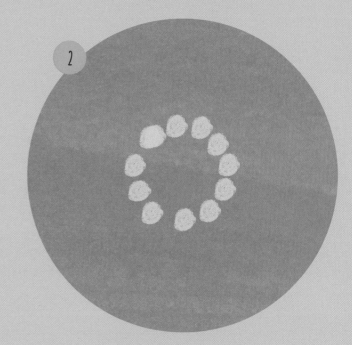

2

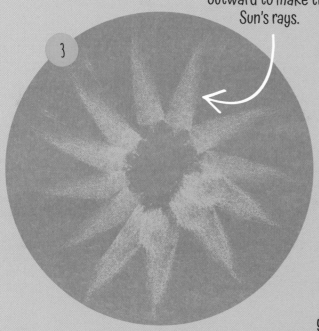

3

Smudge the dots outward to make the Sun's rays.

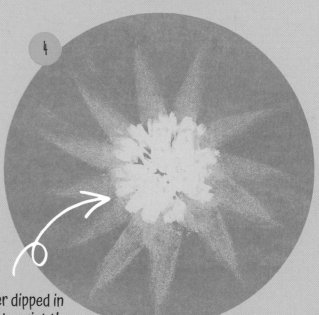

4

Use a flower dipped in yellow paint to print the middle of the Sun.

Add a bright yellow Sun to the summer sky.

iCE CREAM SCOOP

You will need:
Chalks

Roll chalks in a circle to make yummy ice cream scoops.
Do you prefer chocolate , strawberry, or vanilla?

1

Lay a piece of chalk
on its side, and turn it
in a circle.

2

3

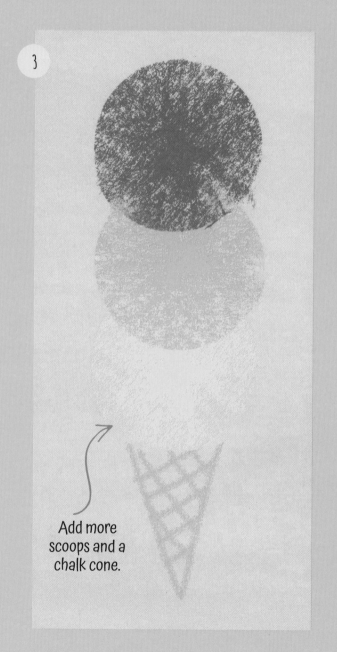

Add more
scoops and a
chalk cone.

Cool down outside with an ice cream sundae.
Add more scoops to the bowl.

BUSY, BUZZY BEES

It's easy to print this lovable bee using your fingertips!

You will need:
Your fingertips
Paints
Pen

1 Start with a black fingerprint.

2 Now layer with a yellow fingerprint.

3

4

5 Make white fingerprint wings with the side of your finger.

6

Print a whole swarm of bees buzzing around this hive!

BOUNCING BUNNIES

Here's how to make cute fingerprint bunnies.
Use thumbprints for the body and a fingerprint for the head.

You will need:
Your fingertips
Paints
Pen

Use thumbprints for
the body.

Print a white fluffy tail
with your little finger.

Make a fingerprint head.

Now make her
a bunny pal!

44

Add some naughty bunnies raiding
the vegetable garden.

POND LIFE PATTERNS

Complete this goldfish and dragonfly with patterned details.

Use bubble wrap to print
scales on the goldfish.

Try and make your wing patterns match on each side.

Draw a pattern in white crayon on the wing,s and wash over it with watery paint.

SEASONAL TREE

You will need:
Your hand
Paintbrush
Paints
Celery slices
Pen

Make this tree with leaves in glorious golds and reds.

1

Make a brown
handprint.
Include some of
your wrist for
the tree trunk.

2

Make celery-
print leaves.

3

Add black
celery prints to
make crows.

4

48

This lawn needs a tree! Add one with lots of leaves and crows.

BRILLIANT BUG

You will need:
Paintbrush
Paints
Apple cut in half
Your fingertips
Pen

Follow the steps to make this super spotted insect.

1

Paint the head and antennae stalks in black.

2 Make the body with a red apple print.

Add black thumbprint spots to the body and to the tops of the antennae.

3

Try making more bugs using thumb and fingerprints, with pen details.

50

Add lots of brilliant bugs to these leaves.

FANTASTIC FUNGI

Make these mushroom prints using real mushrooms!

You will need:
Mushrooms
Paintbrush
Paints
Your fingertips
Bubble wrap

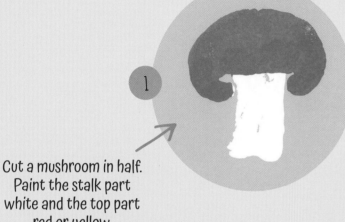

1

Cut a mushroom in half.
Paint the stalk part
white and the top part
red or yellow.
Print on your page with
the flat side down.

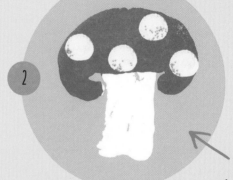

2

Add patterns using
fingerprints or
bubble wrap.

1

2

1

Use the end of a mushroom
stalk to print circles.

52

Fill the forest floor with all kinds of mushrooms.

STORMY SKY

You will need:
Chalks
Your fingertips

Create a thundercloud using this chalk-smudge effect.

1

Use the end of your chalk to make a fluffy cloud shape.

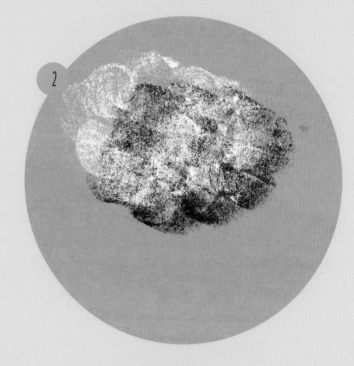

2

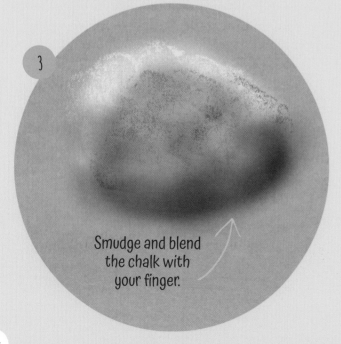

3

Smudge and blend the chalk with your finger.

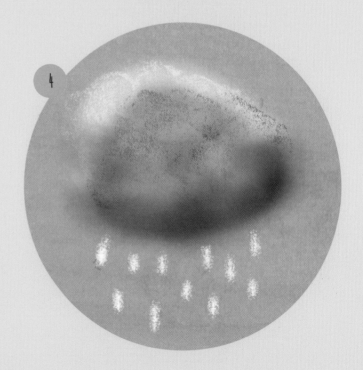

4

It's about to pour with rain! Add thunderclouds
to complete the scene.

RAINING AND POURING

You will need:
Fork
Paints

From a shower to a downpour, you can create all types of rainfall just with fork prints.

1

Dip the tip of the fork in paint.

2

Drag the fork up the page.

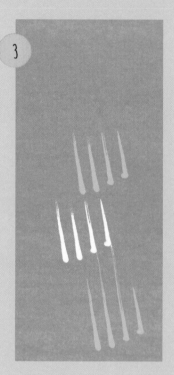

3

1

For thicker drops, put the fork teeth flat in the paint and then print.

2

3

It's raining outside! Add raindrops to the sky.

SPOOKY PUMPKIN

Make your very own Halloween pumpkin with a pepper print and your fingers!

You will need:
Pepper cut in half
Paints
Your fingertips

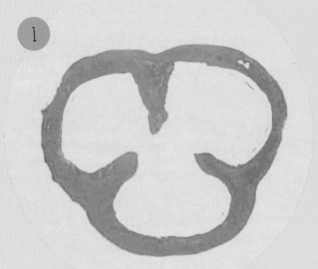

1

Add a smudged green fingerprint for the stalk.

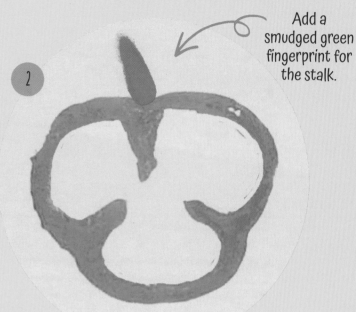

2

Use fingerprints for the face.

3

4

Decorate the doorstep with spooky
pumpkins. Give them each a different face.

SLITHERY SNAIL

Make this cute snail in three simple steps.

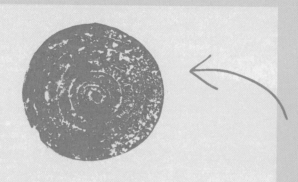

1

Use an onion print for the shell.

2

Use a toothbrush dipped in paint to make the snail's body.

3

Finish with pen.

These leaves are ready for eating.
Add some hungry snails!

SPIKES AND QUILLS

Complete the spikes on this porcupine and hedgehog using fork prints.

You will need:
Fork
Paints

These cute critters need their spikes for protection.

SCAMPERING SQUIRREL

Try your hand at making this chalky squirrel with his bushy tail.

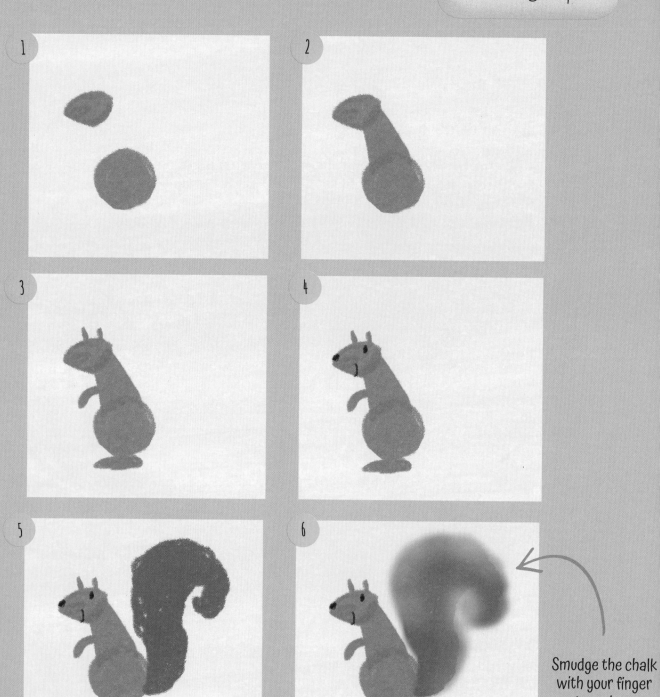

Smudge the chalk with your finger to make a bushy tail.

Add some squirrels gathering acorns in the tree.

HANDY SPIDER

Print this eight-legged creature using two overlapping handprints.
Try not to include your thumb in your handprints.

You will need:
Your hands
Paint
Your fingertips

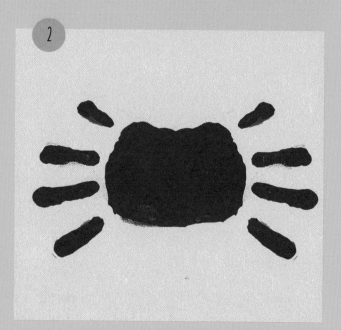

Make white thumbprints
for the eyes.

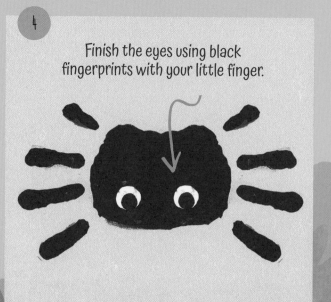

Finish the eyes using black
fingerprints with your little finger.

Add a spider spinning her web.

WONDERFUL WEB

You will need:
Crayons
Paintbrush
Paints

Draw a cobweb in white crayon, and paint over it in watery paint to create a silky spiderweb effect.

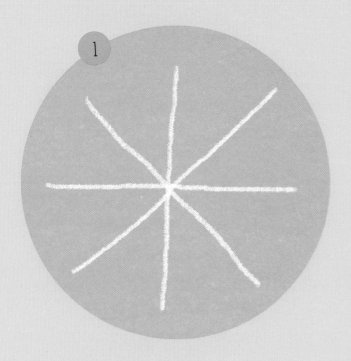

Create a silky web so this hungry spider can catch a fly!

MIDNIGHT OWL

You will need:
Chalks
Your fingertips

Follow these simple steps to create a chalk owl
with a glowing effect.

Smudge the chalk around
the edges to make your
owl glow in the dark!

Add some owls hooting in the moonlight.

FLYING KITE

You will need:
Scissors
Cardboard
Paintbrush
Paints

Print your own kite design in four simple steps.

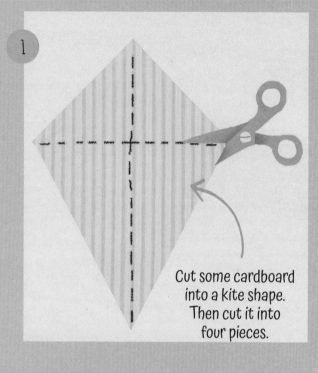

1

Cut some cardboard into a kite shape. Then cut it into four pieces.

2

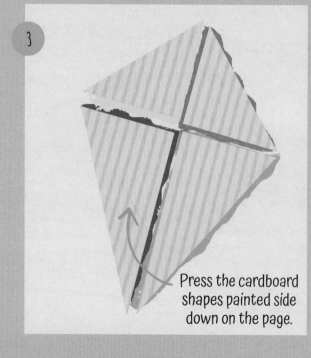

3

Press the cardboard shapes painted side down on the page.

4

Create a display of kites flying high in the sky!

NUTS AND BERRIES

Here's how to make fingerprint nuts, berries, and seeds.

You will need:
Your fingertips
Paints
Pen

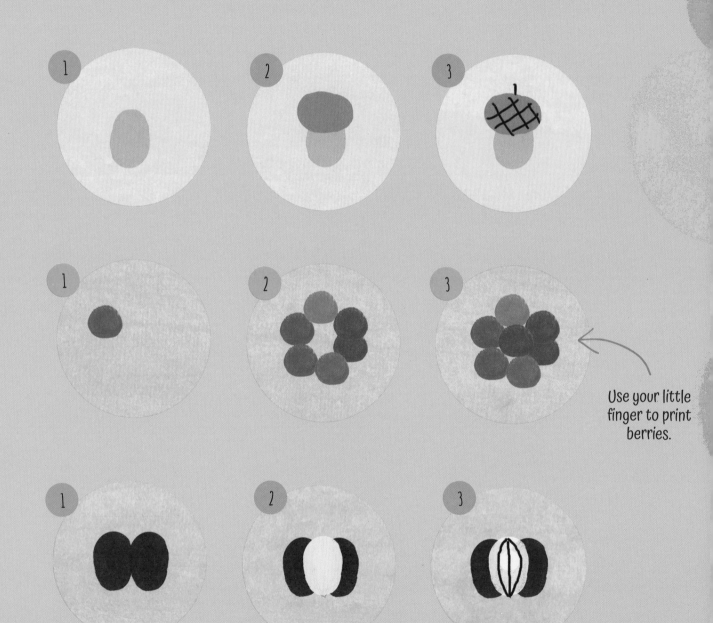

Use your little finger to print berries.

Fill the bush and the feeders with food for hungry animals.

PROUD PEACOCK

Create a prancing peacock on display. Doesn't he look pleased with himself!

You will need:
Paints
Drinking straw
Pen

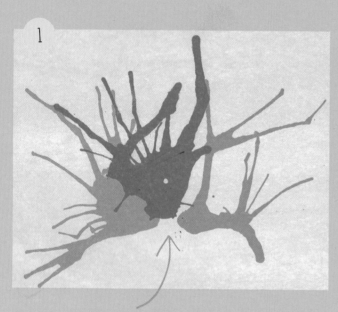

Blow watery green paint up and outward using a straw.

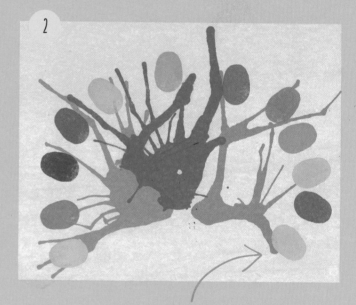

Add fingerprints to decorate the tail.

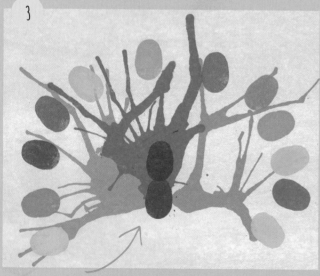

Give him a blue fingerprint head and body.

Add lots of peacocks fanning their feathers.

WINTER TREE

Draw this winter tree in white crayon, then paint over it with a cool blue paint.

You will need:
Crayons
Paintbrush
Paints

1

2

3

4

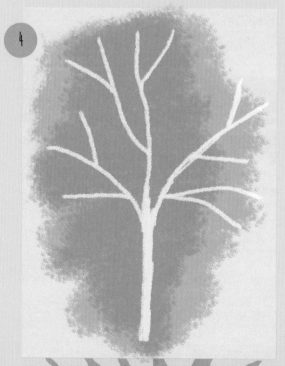

Create a whole forest of frosty trees.

FROSTY THE SNOWMAN

Follow the steps to make a cheerful chalk snowman.

You will need:
Chalks
Your fingertips

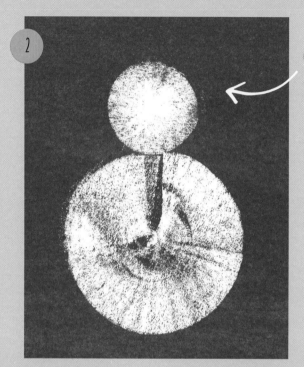

Use a small piece of chalk for the head.

Lay a large piece of chalk on its side, and turn it around in a circle to make the body.

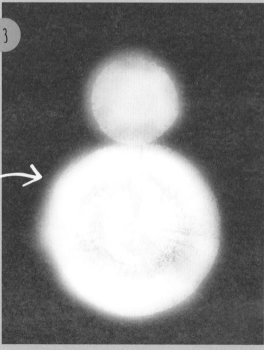

Smudge the chalk with your finger to make a powdery snow effect.

80

Help these children build a snowman!

BURROWING BADGER

You will need:
Your foot
Paintbrush
Paints
Your fingertips

Turn a footprint into a bold badger.

1

Paint the heel of your foot with white paint. Then paint the rest of your foot with black paint, and print.

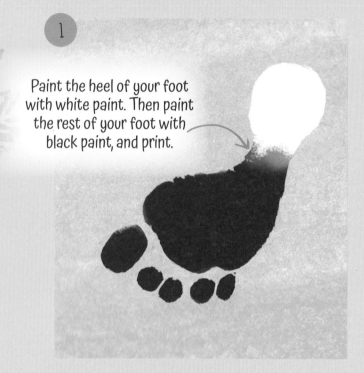

2

Smudge white paint for a tail.

Paint a black stripe on the badger's head.

3

Make a white fingerprint eye and a black fingerprint ear.

4

Paint on black eye, nose, and mouth details.

Print a badger snug in its burrow.

FEATHERED FRIENDS

Give the goose and swan layers of leaf-print feathers.

You will need:
Leaves
Paints
Crayons

Use leaves dipped in paint to make the goose feathers.

Feathers keep birds warm and dry.

Lay leaves under the paper then rub over the top of the paper with the side of a crayon.

ADORABLE DEER

Dip a fork in brown paint to print your deer's body and legs.
Then give it a thumbprint head. Add final details with pen.

You will need:
Fork
Paints
Your fingertips
Pen

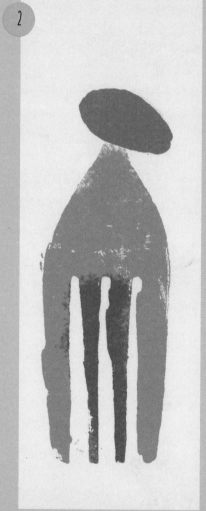

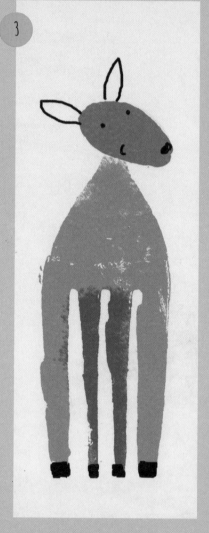

Print a whole herd of deer in the snow.

LET iT SNOW

You will need:
Fork
Paints
Chalks

Layer up icy blue and white fork prints to make these frosty snowflakes.

You can make a Sun using this same technique. Just add some smudged chalk in the middle!

Add a flurry of snowflakes to the snowy sky.
Make a shining sun, too!

FLUFFY MOUSE

You will need:
Half a potato
Paintbrush
Paints
Thick carrot slices
Pen

Create a cute mouse out of vegetable prints in three simple steps.

1

Paint the flat side of half a potato in paint to print the mouse's body.

2

Give your mouse pink carrot-print ears.

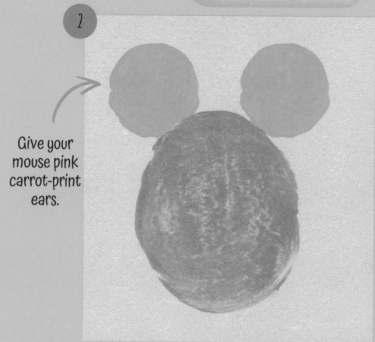

3

Print a family of mice snuggled in the flowerpot.

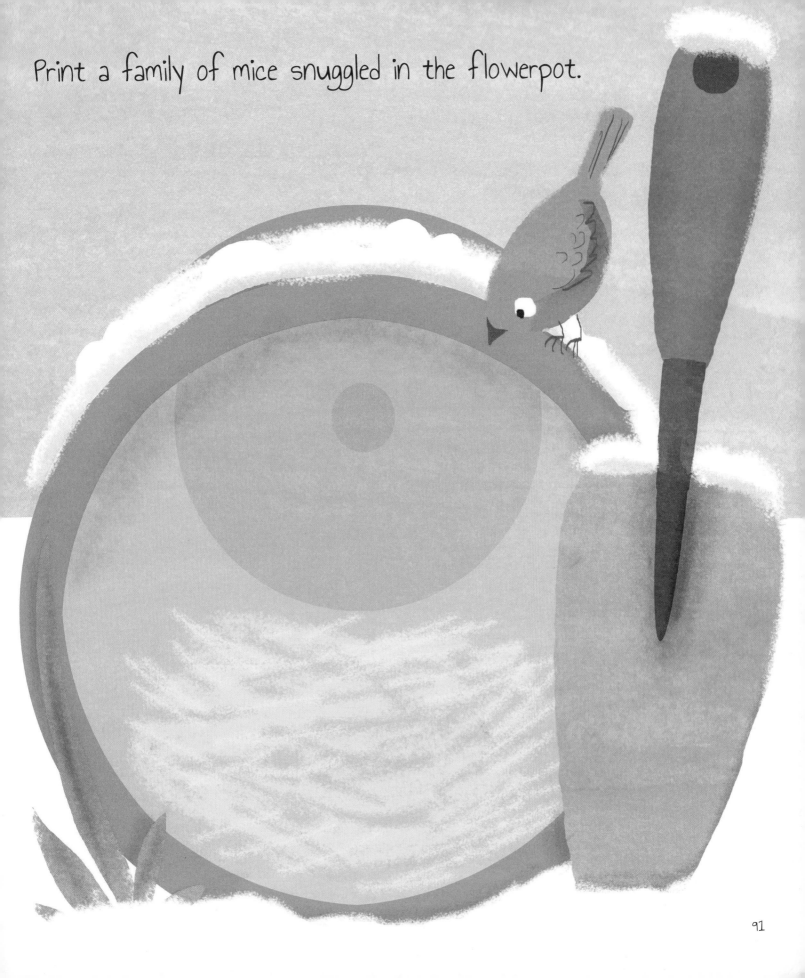

FORK FIR

Make this fabulous fir tree out of fork prints, then decorate it with lights printed with your little finger.

You will need:
Fork
Paints
Your fingertips

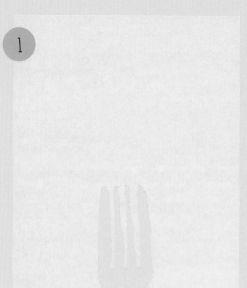

Add some fir trees here, twinkling with lights.

ROBIN REDBREAST

Make prints with your thumb, first finger, and little finger to create three different robins.

You will need:
Your fingertips
Paints
Pen

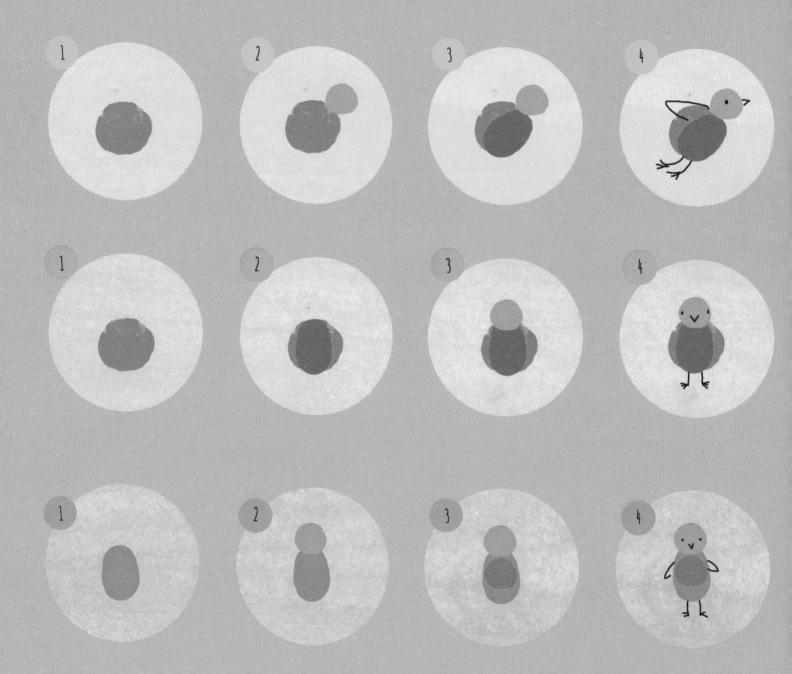

Fill this scene with robins feasting on berries.

SLINKY SNAKE

Paint the side of a bottle cap, then roll it on its side
to print the snake's body. Paint the flat top to print the head.

You will need:
Bottle cap
Paints
Pen

1
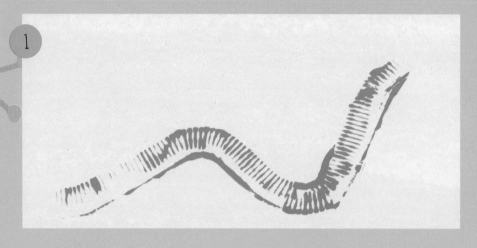

2
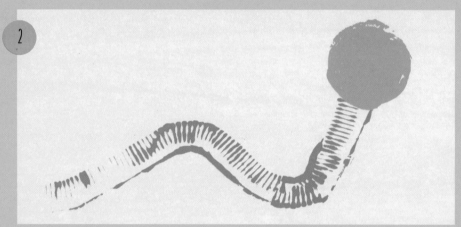

3